The Comrade in White

THE COMRADE IN WHITE

"Lo, I am with you alway"

After the painting by G. Hillyard Swinstead, R. I.

The Comrade in White

BY THE REV.

W. H. LEATHEM, M.A.

INTRODUCTION BY HUGH BLACK

" I shall not fear the battle
If Thou art by my side."

New York   Chicago   Toronto

Fleming H. Revell Company

LONDON AND EDINBURGH

New York: 158 Fifth Avenue
Chicago: 17 North Wabash Ave.
Toronto: 25 Richmond Street, W.
London: 21 Paternoster Square
Edinburgh: 100 Princes Street

INTRODUCTION

THE Great War has put a strain on the resources of human nature, as well as on material resources. Men who have come through the hell of the trenches have discovered some of the secrets of life and death. Many of them have known a reinforcement of spiritual power. It is quite natural that this fact should often be described in emotional form as direct interposition of angels and other supernatural agencies. Among these the most beautiful and tender stories are those of "The Comrade in White." In essence they are all testimony to the perennial fount of strength and comfort of religion—the human need which in all generations

1

has looked up and found God a present help in times of trouble.

The origin of the many stories brought back to England from the battle fronts by her soldiers is that to the average Briton this a religious crusade, and men have gone with an exaltation of soul, willing to make the ultimate sacrifice, willing to die that the world might live. Men and women are face to face with eternal realities, and are driven by the needs of their hearts to the eternal refuge. Unless we see this we miss the most potent fact in the whole situation.

The tender stories in this little volume are a reflex of the great religious stirring of the nation. They describe in a gracious and pathetic way the various abysmal needs of this tragic time, and they indicate how many human souls are finding comfort and healing and strength. They are finding peace as of old, through the assurance that "earth has no sorrows, that heaven cannot heal."

HUGH BLACK.

NEW YORK.

"THE WHITE COMRADE"

I

When soldiers of the Cross waged Holy
    War,
With courage high, and hearts that did not
    quail
Before the foe, in olden times they saw
The blessed vision of the Holy Grail.
Tho' Christ was gone, His pledge was with
    them yet,
For, borne on wings of angels, from the skies,
They saw the chalice that once held the wine
As emblem of the Saviour's sacrifice
For men, and knew that still the Master met,
With His own friends, in fellowship divine.

II

Christ has His soldiers now. Though years
    have rolled
Away, the warriors of the Cross are strong
To fight His battles, as the saints of old,
Against oppression, tyranny, and wrong.

And still amid the conflict, they can trace
The Saviour's influence. Not the Holy Grail
Which once as His remembrance was adored,
But Christ Himself is with them. For a veil
Is lifted from their eyes, and, face to face
They meet the presence of the risen Lord.

III

O blessed vision! After all the years,
Thou'rt with us yet. To-day, as heretofore,
Men see Thee still and they cast off their
   fears,
And take fresh courage to press on once more.
The soldiers, bearing from the desperate
   fight
A wounded brother, see Thee, in the way,
And know Thee for the Saviour, Healer,
   Friend,
For once again, Thy loved ones hear Thee
   say
(O Christ! White Comrade, in their stand for
   right!)
"Lo, I am with you alway, to the end."

                Fidei Defensor.

CONTENTS

7

I

IN THE TRENCHES

"And immediately He talked with them, and saith unto them, " Be of good cheer; it is I; be not afraid."
—THE GOSPEL ACCORDING TO MARK, chap. vi : 50.

" And His raiment was white as snow."
—THE GOSPEL ACCORDING TO MATTHEW, chap. xvii : 2.

" The Battle of Mons, which saved the British Army from annihilation, was, for the most of those who fought with the angels, a sepulchre. They saved the British Army, but they saved it at fearful cost. No ' great host ' withdrew from that field of destruction; the great host strewed the ground with their bodies. Only a remnant of those who stood in the actual furnace of Mons escaped with their lives . . . Let those who mourn, take encouragement from these stories of visions on the battlefield, quietly and with a child's confidence, cultivate within themselves a waiting, receptive and desiring spirit. Let them empty themselves of prejudice and self. . . . Let them detach themselves more and more from the obsessions of worldly life. Serenity is the path by which the thoughts of God travel to us; and Faith is the invitation which brings them to the table of our souls."
—ON THE SIDE OF THE ANGELS.

I

IN THE TRENCHES

STRANGE tales reached us in the trenches. Rumours raced up and down that three-hundred-mile line from Switzerland to the sea. We knew neither the source of them nor the truth of them. They came quickly, and they went quickly. Yet somehow I remember the very hour when George Casey turned to me with a queer look in his blue eyes, and asked if I had seen the Friend of the Wounded.

And then he told me all he knew. After many a hot engagement a man in white had been seen bending over the wounded. Snipers sniped at him. Shells fell all around. Nothing had power to touch him. He was either heroic beyond all heroes, or he was something greater still. This mysterious one, whom the French called *The Comrade in White,* seemed to be everywhere at once. At Nancy, in the Argonne, at Soissons and Ypres, everywhere men were talking of him with hushed voices.

But some laughed and said the trenches were telling on men's nerves. I, who was often reckless enough in my talk, exclaimed that for me seeing was believing, and that I didn't expect any help but an enemy's knife if I was found lying out there wounded.

It was the next day that things got lively on this bit of the front. Our big guns roared from sunrise to sunset, and began again in the morning. At noon we got word to take the trenches in front of us. They were two hundred yards away, and we weren't well started till we knew that the big guns had failed in their work of preparation. It needed a stout heart to go on, but not a man wavered. We had advanced one hundred and fifty yards when we found it was no good. Our Captain called to us to take cover, and just then I was shot through both legs. By God's mercy I fell into a hole of some sort. I suppose I fainted, for when I opened my eyes I was all alone. The pain was horrible, but I didn't dare to move lest the enemy should see me, for they were only fifty yards away, and I did not expect mercy. I was glad when the twilight came. There were men in my own company who would run any risk in the darkness if they thought a comrade was still alive.

The night fell, and soon I heard a step, not stealthy, as I expected, but quiet and firm, as if neither darkness nor death could check those untroubled feet. So little did I guess what was coming that, even when I saw the gleam of white in the darkness, I thought it was a peasant in a white smock, or perhaps a woman deranged. Suddenly, with a little shiver of joy or of fear, I don't know which, I guessed that it was *The*

14

Comrade in White. And at that very moment the enemy's rifles began to shoot. The bullets could scarcely miss such a target, for he flung out his arms as though in entreaty, and then drew them back till he stood like one of those wayside crosses that we saw so often as we marched through France. And he spoke. The words sounded familiar, but all I remember was the beginning. "If thou hadst known," and the ending, "but now they are hid from thine eyes." And then he stooped and gathered me into his arms—me, the biggest man in the regiment—and carried me as if I had been a child.

I must have fainted again, for I woke to consciousness in a little cave by a stream, and *The Comrade in*

White was washing my wounds and binding them up. It seems foolish to say it, for I was in terrible pain, but I was happier at that moment than ever I remember to have been in all my life before. I can't explain it, but it seemed as if all my days I had been waiting for this without knowing it. As long as that hand touched me and those eyes pitied me, I did not seem to care any more about sickness or health, about life or death. And while he swiftly removed every trace of blood and mire I felt as if my whole nature were being washed, as if all the grime and soil of sin were going, and as if I were once more a little child.

I suppose I slept, for when I awoke this feeling was gone. I was a man,

16

and I wanted to know what I could
do for my friend to help him or to
serve him. He was looking towards
the stream, and his hands were
clasped in prayer; and then I saw
that he too had been wounded. I
could see, as it were, a shot-wound
in his hand, and as he prayed a drop
of blood gathered and fell to the
ground. I cried out. I could not
help it, for that wound of his seemed
to me a more awful thing than any
that bitter war had shown me. "You
are wounded too," I said faintly.
Perhaps he heard me, perhaps it was
the look on my face, but he answered
gently, "This is an old wound, but it
has troubled me of late." And then
I noticed sorrowfully that the same
cruel mark was on his feet. You will

17

wonder that I did not know sooner. I wonder myself. But it was only when I saw His feet that I knew Him.

"The Living Christ"—I had heard the Chaplain speak of Him a few weeks before, but now I knew that He had come to me—to me who had put Him out of my life in the hot fever of my youth. I was longing to speak and to thank Him, but no words came. And then He rose swiftly and said, "Lie here to-day by the water. I will come for you to-morrow. I have work for you to do, and you will do it for me."

In a moment He was gone. And while I wait for Him I write this down that I may not lose the memory of it. I feel weak and lonely and

18

my pain increases, but I have His promise. I know that He will come for me to-morrow.

II

THE MESSENGER

" And as they thus spake, Jesus himself stood in the midst of them, and saith unto them, Peace be unto you."

—THE GOSPEL ACCORDING TO LUKE, chap. xxiv : 36.

" The War has powerfully changed the ' psychological atmosphere,' and the thoughts of a great multitude are turned towards the spiritual aspect of existence. In this vast but connected universe we are not the only self-conscious beings. Life is working here as elsewhere, for some sublime purpose. The day is at hand when we shall turn from the child-like amusements and excitements of physical science to the unimaginable adventures of super-physical discovery; and in that day we shall not only flash our messages to the stars, but hold communion with our dead."

—HAROLD BEGBIE.

II

THE MESSENGER

THE Parish Church stood high perched in the Glen, and through its clear windows we could see the white, winding road that was our one link with the great world beyond the mountains. Perhaps our eyes strayed from the preacher's face more than was seemly, and in spring time we had this excuse, that the fresh green of the larches against the dark rocks made a picture fairer to the eye than our plain old Church and its high pulpit.

But that Sunday in the spring of

the Great War the minister had us
all, even the young and thoughtless,
in the hollow of his hand. It was
the 18th chapter of Second Samuel
that he had read earlier in the Service, and now he was opening its
meaning to us with deep-felt real-
isation of those great dramatic epi-
sodes.

We saw the young man Absalom
die. We saw Cushi start to bear his
tidings to the king. We watched
Ahimaaz swift on his track. We
marked the king's anxious waiting,
and the fixed gaze of the watchman
on the city walls. We strained in
the long strain of the runners. We
fainted with the fears of a father's
heart. We saw Ahimaaz outrun his
rival yet falter in his message. And

24

we heard the blow upon David's heart of Cushi's stroke. "And the king said unto Cushi, Is the young man Absalom safe? And Cushi answered, The enemies of my lord the king, and all that rise against thee to do thee hurt, be as that young man is."

There were tears in the women's eyes as the preacher called us to see the stricken and weeping king climbing with weary step to the chamber over the gate. And in a solemn hush we heard the cry of his anguish "—O my son Absalom! my son, my son Absalom! would God I had died for thee. O Absalom, my son, my son!"

We had anxious fathers and mothers and wives and sisters in the

25

Church that day, and it was as though our own sorrows were all gathered up into the old, unhappy, far-off things of which the preacher spoke. I had a dear one to be concerned for, but I was thinking now of some one else. For Widow M'Donald was there, and the days had grown into weeks since last she had tidings of John—and he was her only boy.

Suddenly she rose and slipped out. I followed her, for there was an odd, silent friendship between us, and I thought that I might help. To my surprise she did not turn homewards, but down the Glen, and there I saw that some one was waiting for her by the pine wood. "I saw your sign, sir," she said, "and I guessed you brought news of John. Oh, sir, tell me quick, is he safe?"

"He is safe," the stranger answered. I could not see His face, but He seemed weary and far-travelled. It was His voice that made me wonder. For as He said "safe," it was as a new word to me, so full of healing and of peace that it laid to rest every fear of my unquiet heart.

"And will he be home soon?" It was the mother who was speaking now.

"I have taken the dear lad home," answered the stranger. "His room has been long prepared for him in my Father's house. He has fought a good fight. He was wounded, but his wounds are healed. He **was**

27

weary, but he has found rest." And so speaking He looked at us, and as the mother clasped my hand I knew that the truth was breaking on her too.

"He is dead," she sobbed.

"No," said the stranger, "he is alive, for he has laid down his life that he might take it again."

There was silence then, and the stranger turned to leave us. Even in her grief the mourner was mindful of what was due to Him who had taken upon Himself the burden of sorrowful tidings.

"Come back with us, and break bread, and rest a while," she said, "for, sir, you seem spent, and it is out of a kind heart that you have spoken."

28

"I may not tarry," He made answer, "for there are many who need me, and I must go to them, but for thy comfort thou shalt first know who hath brought thee tidings of thy son's passage through death to life."

I dare not try to tell what happened then under the shadow of the pines, but somehow we *knew* our eyes looked into the face of the soldiers' *The Comrade in White;* and we knew Him. And then His hand was lifted in blessing, and we heard this word, that is now as the music of our daily lives: "Peace I leave with you, my peace I give unto you: not as the world giveth, give I unto you. Let not your heart be troubled, neither let it be afraid."

We walked in a strange, calm silence to the widow's cottage, and then as we parted she turned to me a face filled with heavenly peace— "My dear boy lives," she said.

III

MAIMED OR PERFECTED?

"Now no chastening for the present seemeth to be joyous but grievous: nevertheless, afterward, it yieldeth the peaceable fruit of righteousness unto them which are exercised thereby."

—HEBREWS xii : 11.

"Six months passed within the danger zone, produces a subtle but marked change. Bright lads become men, who bear all the marks of having passed through a solemn purification by fire. And the subtle influence, as thus depicted, is communicated to us. . . . To say that the horrors of war have subdued and overawed them is but part of the explanation. It seems nearer to the truth to add, that these harrowing experiences, whatever they may have been, have only helped to make our young men susceptible to spiritual influences of the highest quality. In fine, they have been following in the footsteps of Him who is The Great Sacrifice, and even amid the bursting shells have caught a glimpse of wounds that transform and consecrate their own."

—*The Great Sacrifice*, JOHN ADAMS.

III

MAIMED OR PERFECTED?

MY heart grew bitter in me when the news came of Harry's operation. I had been half relieved when I heard that he was wounded, and that the wound was not dangerous. For the grim alternative was seldom out of my thoughts, and at least his dear life was safe. Now I was crushed by the brave, pathetic letter in which he told me that his right leg had been amputated, and that he was lucky to get off so easily. That made me rebellious and **very, very** bitter. And it was against **God**

that I felt worst—God who had allowed this unthinkable thing to be.

Harry a cripple! Harry of all people! I could not imagine it, nor accept it, nor even face the truth of it. And away at the bottom of my heart lurked the thought that it had been better for himself that he had died in the strength and beauty of his manhood. Why should his spirit be doomed to live on in a ruined home?

Harry is my only brother, and he has been my hero always. Manliness, strength, courage, unselfishness —I know what these things mean; they mean Harry. And of course I was proud when he got his double blue at Cambridge. Cricket and football were more than pastimes to him. He put his heart and soul into them, and when he made 106 not out against Oxford he was as happy as if he had found a new continent. And now the great athlete, the pride of his College, the big clean-limbed giant was a cripple. I could not weep for it, because I could not believe it. I took the thought and flung it from me. And then I picked it up again, and gazed at it with hard, unseeing eyes. It was at that time I stopped praying. What was prayer but a mockery, if Harry was maimed?

Harry was at Cairo, and I could not go to him. And though that made me feel helpless, and almost mad with inaction, yet in my heart I dreaded meeting him, seeing him,

35

taking in the bitterness of it through the eyes. I was a coward, you see, and my love for him a poor thing at the best. But there are some who will understand how I felt, and will forgive me.

His letters were all right, not a word of complaint, for Harry never grumbled, and many a good story of the hospital and its patients and its staff. But there was something else, a kind of gentle seriousness as if life were different now. And I read my own misery into that, and pictured him a man devoured by a secret despair, while he smiled his brave undefeated smile in the face of all the world.

The weeks passed, and I braced myself for the coming ordeal. Then

everything came with a rush at the
last, and there I was at the docks
giving my brave soldier his welcome
home. It was not any easier than I
expected. I tried my hardest, as you
may guess, to be all joy and bright-
ness, but when we were alone in the
motor together my eyes were full of
tears, and I broke down utterly. Poor
Harry, poor Harry, why are physical calamities so awful and so ir-
revocable?

He let me cry, and then he said
suddenly, "Come, Mary, look at the
real 'me,' don't bother about that old
leg, but look into my face, and tell
me what you see. There is something good for you to see if you will
look for it."

He said it so strangely that I was
37

myself in a moment, and doing what he told me just as in the good old days before the war. And then I saw that Harry was a new Harry altogether, and that he was radiantly happy. His face was pale and thin, but his eyes were ablaze with something mysterious and wonderful. "Don't ask me anything now," he said; "wait till we are in my old den, and then I will tell you everything." And by this time I was so comforted that I was content to lie back and watch that dear, happy face of his.

I shall never forget the talk we had afterwards. "Mary," he said, in his straight, direct way, "I've come back a better man. I have been all my life a healthy, happy pagan. We were brought up, you and I, on the theory of a healthy mind in a healthy body, and, of course, it's a good theory so far as it goes. But it did for me what it does for many a fellow. It made me forget my soul. Sport did a lot for me, I know, but sport became my world. The life I lived there was wholesome enough, but at the best what a poor, contracted, limited thing is the body, and its joy. And what a big, splendid world I've found the door to now."

"How did it come about, Harry?" I said, and the frost and the bitterness and the anger against God were all gone out of my heart and voice.

"Well, I don't quite know. That's the queer thing about it. I don't deny I was a bit savage at first at what had happened. And I often

wished I were dead, for I saw my old
self wasn't much good for this new
life I was up against. Then one Sunday the padre, who was a very decent
sort, gave us a straight talk that
opened my eyes a bit. He was
speaking about Paul and the differ-
ence Christ made in his life. Paul
was a splendid fellow, and as good
as good could be, and just like many
a man to-day who seems all right
without Christ. But what a differ-
ence Christ made in him for all that!
And how He made the old Saul of
Tarsus seem a poor thing in com-
parison with Paul the apostle! There
was something, too, about Paul's
thorn in the flesh, but I forget that
bit. Anyhow I did some furious
thinking that Sunday in Cairo,

though I saw nothing clearly, and didn't lay much store by my own future.

"That night the strange thing happened. I woke up in the early hours when no one was astir, and I saw a man come in by the door and walk down the ward. He gave a sort of understanding, tender look at every face as he passed, and when he saw that I was awake he came close beside me and held my hand for a moment. Then he said, 'Will you let me help you with this burden of yours?' I thought at first it was the new doctor we were expecting. Then I knew quite suddenly that it was *The Comrade in White,* and that He wanted me very much to say 'Yes.' And as I said it I felt the first real happiness that I had known since I was wounded. And then He smiled and went away.

"I told myself next day that it was a dream, and perhaps it was, but that strange, odd happiness has never left me since. I wouldn't be back again in the old way, not for all the world could give me, not even to have my leg restored."

"And is He really helping you with your burden?" I whispered.

"Why, Mary child, can't you see," he exclaimed, with his merry laugh; "can't you see that He has carried my burden quite away? I was but half a man before. He has made me whole."

IV

THE PRAYER CIRCLE

" . . . More things are wrought by prayer
Than this world dreams of. Wherefore, let thy
   voice
Rise like a fountain for me night and day.
For what are men better than sheep or goats
That nourish a blind life within the brain,
If, knowing God, they lift not hands of prayer
Both for themselves and those who call them
   friend?
For so the whole round earth is every way
Bound by gold chains about the feet of God."
—*The Passing of Arthur*, ALFRED, LORD TENNYSON.

" Fight the good fight with all thy might,
   Christ is thy strength, and Christ thy right,
   Lay hold on life, and it shall be
   Thy joy and crown eternally.

         .   .   .   .   .

" Faint not, nor fear, His arms are near,
   He changeth not, and thou art dear:
   Only believe, and thou shalt see
   That Christ is all in all to thee."
                     —J. S. B. MONSELL.

IV

THE PRAYER CIRCLE

LIEUTENANT ROGER
FENTON had a lump in his
throat when he said good-bye to his
boys. There they were in a bunch
on the station platform, the ten way-
ward lads into whom he had sought
to instil the fear of God on Tuesday
evenings in winter, and with whom
he had rambled and played cricket
every Saturday afternoon in sum-
mer. Boys of fourteen to seventeen
are a tough proposition, and though
Fenton would answer for their bowl-
ing and batting he wasn't over san-

guine about their religion. But they had filled a big place in his lonely life in the dull little country town, and now he had to leave them and lose them. For the great call had reached him, and be bore the King's commission, and in his heart of hearts he had the feeling that he would never come back.

Now the chaff and the parting words of good luck were over, and the train was panting to be off. "Boys," he cried suddenly, "I want you to do something for me, something hard." "Anything you like, sir," they answered eagerly. But their faces fell when they heard their teacher's word. "Look here," he said, "it's this. You'll meet in the old place every Tuesday evening for

46

a few minutes and pray for me that I may do my duty, and, if it please God, that I may come back to you all. And I'll pray for you at the same time even if I'm in the thick of battle. Is it a bargain?"

I wish you had seen the dismay on those ten faces. It was any odds on their blurting out a shamefaced refusal, but Ted Harper, their acknowledged chief, pulled himself together just in time, and called out as the train began to move:—"We'll do it, sir. I don't know how we'll manage it, but we'll do our best. We'll not go back on you."

As Fenton sank into his corner he was aware of the mocking looks of his brother officers. "I say," said one of them, "you don't really think

those chaps are going to hold a
prayer-meeting for you every week,
and if they did you can't believe it
would stop an enemy's bullet or turn
an enemy's shell. It's all very well
to be pious, but that's a bit too
thick." Fenton flushed, but he took
it in good part. "Prayer's a big bit
of our religion," he said, "and I've a
notion these prayers will help me.
Anyhow I'm sure my lads will do
their part. Where Ted Harper
leads, they follow."

And sure enough the boys did their
part. It was fine to see them start-
ing out in the wrong direction, and
twisting and doubling through the
crooked lanes till they worked round
to the Mission Hall, and then in with
a rush and a scuttle, that as few as

48

possible might see. The doings of the Fenton crowd, as they were known locally, were the talk of the town in those first days after Roger departed. Would they meet? Would they keep it up? Would they bear the ridicule of the other boys of their own age? And how in the world would they pray?

Time answered all these questions except the last. They met, they continued to meet, they faced ridicule like heroes. But how did they pray? That mystery was as deep and insoluble as before, for whatever awful oath of secrecy bound them to silence not a whisper of the doings of those Tuesday evenings was divulged to the outside world.

I was the only one who ever knew,

and I found out by chance. Ted
Harper had borrowed "Fights for
the Flag" from me, and when I got
it back there was a soiled piece of
paper in it with something written
in Ted's ungainly hand. I thought
he had been copying a passage, and
anxious to see what had struck him,
I opened the sheet out and read
these words:—"O God, it's a hard
business praying. But Roger made
me promise. And you know how decent he's been to me and the crowd.
Listen to us now, and excuse the
wrong words, and bring him back
safe. And, O God, make him the
bravest soldier that ever was, and
give him the V. C. That's what we all
want for him. And don't let the war
be long, for Christ's sake. Amen."

I felt a good deal ashamed of myself when I came to the end of this artless prayer. I had got their secret. I could see them kneeling round the Mission forms, two or three with crumpled papers in their hands. They were unutterably shy of religious expression, and to read was their only chance. The boys on whom the fatal lot fell the previous Tuesday were bound to appear with their written devotions a week later. This war has given us back the supernatural, but no miracle seems more wonderful to me than those ten lads and their ill-written prayers. And, remember, that liturgical service lasted six months, and never a break in the Tuesday meeting. What a grand thing a boy's heart is, when

you capture its loyalty and its af-
fection!

It was a black day when the news
came. The local Territorials had advanced too far on the wing of a great
offensive, and had been almost an-
nihilated. The few survivors had
dug themselves in, and held on till
that bitter Tuesday faded into darkness and night. When relief came,
one man was left alive. He was
wounded in four places, but he was
still loading and firing, and he wept
when they picked him up and carried
him away for first aid. That solitary
hero, absolutely the only survivor of
our local regiment, was Lieutenant
Roger Fenton, V. C.

When his wounds were healed,
and the King had done the needful

bit of decoration, we got him home.
We did not make the fuss they did
in some places. Our disaster was
too awful, and the pathos of that
solitary survivor too piercing. But
some of us were at the station, and
there in the front row were the ten
men of prayer. Poor Roger quite
broke down when he saw them. And
he could find no words to thank them.
But he wrung their hands till they
winced with the pain of that iron
grip.

That night I got a chance of a
talk with him alone. He was too
modest to tell me anything of his
own great exploit. But there was
evidently something he wanted to say,
and it was as if he did not know how
to begin. At last he said, "I have a

story to tell that not one in fifty would listen to. That Tuesday evening when I was left alone, and had given up all hope, I remembered it was the hour of the old meeting, and I kept my promise and prayed for the boys of my Class. Then everything around me faded from my mind, and I saw the dear lads in the Mission Room at prayer. I don't mean that I went back in memory. I knew with an absolute certainty that I was there invisible in that night's meeting. Whether in the body or out of the body, I cannot say, but there I was, watching and listening."

"How wonderful!" I said.

"That's not all, there's something stranger still," he went on. "They were kneeling on the floor, and Ted

Harper was reading a prayer, and when it was done they said 'Amen' as with one voice. I counted to see if they were all there. I got to ten right enough, but I did not stop there. I counted again, and this is the odd thing—*there were eleven of them!* In my dream or vision or trance, call it what you will, I was vaguely troubled by this unexpected number. I saw the ten troop out in their old familiar way, and I turned back to find the eleventh, *The Comrade in White,* and to speak to Him. I felt His presence still, and was glad of it, for the trouble and perplexity were all gone and in their place a great expectation. I seemed to know the very place where He had been kneeling, and I hurried forward.

55

But there was nothing to be seen, nothing but the well-remembered text staring down at me from the wall—'For where two or three are gathered together in my name, there am I in the midst of them.' I remembered no more, till I found myself in the base hospital. But of course I knew then how I had been saved, and what my boys had done for me.

"It makes a man feel strange to have his life given back to him like that; it's as if God would expect a great deal in return. But there's a stronger feeling still in my heart. I believe the lads got their answer not for my sake but for their own. Think what it means to them. They've got their feet now on the rock of prayer. They know the truth of God. I'm not sure, but I don't think I'll ever tell them that I saw Christ in their midst. They know it in their own way, and perhaps their own way is best."

And as he said it, I saw that Lieutenant Roger Fenton was prouder of his boys than of his Victoria Cross.